Published by Playdead Press 2017

A CIP catalogue record for this book is available from the British Library.

ISBN 978-1-910067-52-9

Playdead Press
www.playdeadpress.com

Cover design: Ben Styles
Photo: Jon Foxley- Evans
***The Book of Darkness & Light* logo design:** Wayne Gamble

For Anna.
For everything.

CAST & CREATIVE TEAM

Adam Z. Robinson | Writer and The Storyteller

Ben Styles | Composer and The Musician

Dick Bonham | Dramaturg

Rachel Ashwanden | Technical Stage Manager

Aly Howe | Lighting and Technical Design (2017 tour)

LittleMighty | Producer

ADAM Z. ROBINSON | WRITER AND THE STORYTELLER

Adam Z. Robinson is a storyteller and a writer of theatre, short fiction and film. His latest show *Shivers* is a new collection of ghost stories from **The Book of Darkness & Light**. The play is a co-production with Square Chapel Arts Centre, Halifax, and Harrogate Theatres. It is produced by LittleMighty, premiering at Square Chapel Arts Centre in September 2017. *Shivers* will tour in autumn 2018. Adam co-wrote *Seaside Terror* with Odd Doll Puppetry, touring in autumn 2017. He is one of the writers on Common Chorus's *A Wind of Change*. Adam's short film *The Split* was directed by Ed Rigg (*Confection, Passenger*) and starred Edward Hogg (*Taboo, Indian Summers*). It has screened at several international film festivals including the Manchester Film Festival, Berlin's 'British Shorts' festival, the Cambridge Film Festival and the London Short Film Festival. Adam co-wrote and co-directed the short film *Go On, My Son* (with Nick Coupe), which was supported by Roundhouse, London. Adam's play *Conscientious* toured nationally in 2014. The show was directed by Alex Chisholm and performed by Rachel Ashwanden. He is the author of *Bad House* (NSDF 2010 – co-written with Lucy Arnold) and *Little Red* (Edinburgh Fringe 2008).

BEN STYLES | COMPOSER AND THE MUSICIAN

Ben Styles is a musician and composer, publishing editor and software developer. He has been playing music since the age of 7. While at university, he found a violin in a friend's attic and set himself the challenge of teaching himself to play it. Within a year he had joined a band, **Backyards**. The band played the BBC Introducing stages at Leeds and Reading Festival. They had several releases, including *If You're Scared*, *Underbank Hall* and *Goodhart's Law*. *The Book of*

Darkness & Light was Ben's first theatre project and he will collaborate with Adam Z. Robinson again on *Shivers*, a series of brand new ghost stories.

DICK BONHAM | DRAMATURG

Dick Bonham is an experienced director, dramaturg and producer. As a director he has an ongoing partnership with Daniel Bye, recently directing the Fringe First Award winning *Going Viral*, as well as previous pieces *The Price of Everything* and *How to Occupy An Oil Rig*. Other projects include Matthew Bellwood's *An Icy Man*, which premiered at the West Yorkshire Playhouse, and Emma Decent's *Beyond Dreams of Aberystwyth* (The Lowry, Salford Quays and touring). He wrote and directed *We Can Be Heroes*, which toured nationally in 2015. He is currently developing his own show *Thinner Blood* with York Theatre Royal and is writing *If I Say Jump* for Common Chorus Theatre.

RACHEL ASHWANDEN | TECHNICAL STAGE MANAGER

Rachel Ashwanden is a performer and stage manager. She has worked with *The Book of Darkness & Light* as a technician and stage manager since 2015. In 2014 she performed the monologue *Conscientious* by Adam Z. Robinson. The show toured nationally and was revived in 2016 for a run of special performances in collaboration with the University of Leeds Special Collections. Rachel was a member of the National Youth Theatre from 2006. She has appeared in two independent productions at the Edinburgh Fringe – *Poets' Corner* (2009) and *Wrens* (2011). In 2012, she appeared in *You The Player* – part of the Transform Festival at West Yorkshire Playhouse – and has subsequently been involved in the theatre's Summer Sublets programme and Furnace Festival. Since finishing her English and Theatre Studies degree at the University of Leeds she has worked in disability arts and education, and was a Workshop Leader with the creative education group Purple Patch Arts, teaching adults with learning disabilities.

ALY HOWE | LIGHTING AND TECHNICAL DESIGN (2017 TOUR)

Aly Howe is a stage manager and touring and in-house technician. Her credits include working with companies such as Red Ladder on *Big Society* (2012) and *The Damned United* (2017 Tour). She works and tours with a number of LittleMighty associate companies such as Luna Bug, Odd Doll, Most Wanted, Sometimes We Play, as well as various other performers and theatre makers in and around the North of England. She also occasionally dabbles in a bit of contemporary dance and opera.

LITTLEMIGHTY | PRODUCER

LittleMighty is an independent producer based in Leeds that works nationally with remarkable artists to make brilliant theatre happen. Their recent successes include Silent Uproar's Kevin Spacey Award-winning *A Super Happy Story (About Feeling Super Sad)* at the Edinburgh Fringe; Unfolding Theatre's *Putting the Band Back Together* (Journal Culture Awards: Best Performance); and Testament's *Blake Remixed* (co-production with West Yorkshire Playhouse). www.littlemighty.co.uk

THE BOOK OF DARKNESS & LIGHT

The Book of Darkness & Light was created by writer Adam Z. Robinson and musician Ben Styles. Originally conceived for Light Night Leeds, 2015, the premise was simple: original, gothic tales told live to the sounds of the violin. At that first event, over 1,500 people came to see and listen to a ghost story told in the beautiful, atmospheric surroundings of Leeds's oldest church.

Afterwards, Adam and Ben went on to create a 'Ghost stories for Christmas' show which played two sell-out performances at the Hyde Park Book Club, Leeds. In June 2016, the show received funding from Arts Council England for a tour in autumn/winter of that year, visiting libraries, theatres and arts spaces. The show received further support from Arts Council England to play at 23 theatres on their 2017 national tour.

A follow-up to *The Book of Darkness & Light* is currently being developed in association with Square Chapel Arts Centre, Harrogate Theatres and LittleMighty. *Shivers*, a brand new trio of ghost stories, will premiere in September 2017 at Square Chapel Arts Centre before a run of four performances at Harrogate Theatre in January 2018. The show will tour in autumn 2018.

www.thebookofdarknessandlight.com

INTRODUCTION
Adam Z. Robinson

I was eight when I experienced my first 'campfire ghost story'. Except, there was no fire. And we were camping in my big brother's friend's back garden in Halifax. Just before 'lights out', the friend's auntie came out to say goodnight to us intrepid adventurers. She told us her own version of W. W. Jacobs' 'The Monkey's Paw'. It was many years later, after I'd read the original story, that I realised she'd re-invented the whole tale (with the eponymous paw being more or less the only common factor). But it didn't matter. I was absolutely terrified. And absolutely delighted. From that moment, I sought out ghost stories wherever I could find them.

I used to love hearing 'true' ghost stories as a kid, too. Whether it was a tale of the touch of an icy hand at the top of a staircase, a grey lady walking the halls of the school library or a disembodied voice whispering from the darkness of a bedroom, I was always riveted. Everyone seemed to have one of these stories, too, and because there was never any doubt in the teller's mind that these supernatural accounts were true - that they had all *actually happened* - the tension and the terror were always at fever pitch. The stories sparked with drama; I ate them up. This regular exchange of spooky yarns evidently had a big impact on me.

I remember two books that we had growing up which fanned the flames. The first was *The World's Greatest: Ghosts*. It was part of a series including *The World's Greatest: UFO Sightings, Serial Killers, Mistakes, Disasters* and *Mysteries* (what qualified as 'great' was perhaps the greatest mystery of them all). The book belonged to my brother but I used to borrow it all the time, reading it over and over, soaking up the weird details and trying to learn my favourite stories to tell to friends. There was a particularly chilling tale about a headless cyclist which I shared at a scout camp when I was ten. It fell flat. I think I messed up the ending (the best bit).

The other book was *True Horror Stories* by Terry Deary (of Horrible Histories fame). I'd bought it at a primary school book fair when I was in Year 5. It terrified me. Even the cover, with its illustration of a be-horned anthropomorphised, skeletal horse-monster emerging from billowing smoke, its black cloak swishing about it gave me goosebumps. Again, I couldn't get enough of the stories. The way Deary took these creepy, purportedly true incidents and wove them into brilliantly-gripping tales was something I admired and wanted to emulate, even at that age. I still have the book. I still find it terrifying.

Later, at college and university, I discovered the masters of gothic short fiction: M.R. James, Elizabeth Gaskell, E. Nesbit, Hugh Walpole, Edgar Allen Poe, Robert Louis Stephenson, Edith Wharton (to name only a handful) and my love affair with the literary ghost story really began. I still greedily guzzle down ghost stories on a regular basis (glutting, particularly, in December when I have a self-imposed tradition of reading a different ghost story each day of advent), but I feel the very best way to enjoy these unquiet tales is to hear them told aloud. Nothing beats it.

With **The Book of Darkness & Light** we are always trying to replicate the cosy jeopardy you felt as a child listening to a ghost story. The uncanny joy of being simultaneously spooked and captivated by a chilling tale, preferably told in a canvas tent by Auntie Anne in your brother's friend's back garden in

Halifax. With every show we try to bring the fun of being frightened to the stage.

The Book of Darkness & Light is a labour of love. Writing and performing these stories alongside Ben is not only the best job I've ever had, it's one of the things I love doing most in the world. So, do keep coming. We have many more tales to tell.

THANK YOU

I'd sincerely like to thank the following...

The other half of The Book of Darkness & Light, Ben Styles, for being unbelievably dedicated, passionate and talented - the magic of the TBODAL live show is due to his beautifully-haunting score. Anna Wiseman to whom this book is dedicated, for being constantly supportive, kind, patient, encouraging and for offering an unimaginable amount of belief in me and all of this. I could not do any of it without her. Danielle Parkinson for many, many reasons and for being so supportive of Ben and me throughout this project. Rachel Ashwanden for being a hugely important part of the TBODAL family. Our producers LittleMighty for putting everything together behind the scenes. Dick Bonham for outstanding direction, dramaturgy, advice and friendship over the years, and for endless enthusiasm for everything Gothic. Andy Craven-Griffiths, Nick Coupe, Andrew Dobbie and Ed Rigg for being the being the people I bounce most ideas off and for constant sage advice. Paul and Sue Styles for their support leading up to the first performance of this show. Lynn Bauman-Milner, Stacey Harrower, Jimmy Robertson (who brought Ben and me together in the first place) and Emily Slater-Chandler for proof-reading the book. Ali Ford, Sam

Mitchell, Martin Clarke, Angus Froste, Sofia Cann and everyone at Square Chapel. Emma McDowell and everyone at Harrogate Theatres. Jon Foxley-Evans and Paul Haydock for the trailer and photography. Matt Angove, Porl Cooper, Alan Lane, Sally Proctor and Joanna Resnick at Slung Low. Christine Holgate and all at North Yorkshire Libraries. Rhian Isaac and Ross Horsley at Leeds Central Library. Max Dorey for being my partner in crime on *Tales from the Red Barn,* where early versions of 'Girl, Dancing' and 'Plagued' originally appeared. Chris Hicks for huge amounts of help, insight, research and expertise on roundhouse lock-ups. Jill Bullock for friendship, support, belief and dropped calls (even though this book will be too scary for her to read). Andy Craven-Griffiths and Rachel Ashwanden for being the bonehouse prisoners. Wayne Gamble for our fantastic tour print design and logo. Aly Howe for designing our 2017 tour lighting. Nick Lane for introducing us to Playdead Press. Elliot Robinson for making the whole publication process incredibly straightforward for us. Arts Council England for their generous support of the tours. Amazing teachers over the years: Carol Stoker, Lin Devine, Dave Davies, Jane Becker, Denis Flannery, Bridget Bennett. Everyone who has been to see *The Book of Darkness & Light* live. And finally to my family and friends for their support and for coming along to the shows.

And of course... you! For buying this book. Thank you.

A NOTE ON PERFORMANCE

In the original production The Storyteller maintained a single, unique persona for each story – i.e. the narrator of each tale. There are, however, several other character voices throughout the tales which can be presented as audio recordings (as in the original production) or The Storyteller can perform these parts him/herself. Other actors may be used for these sections, if preferred.

CHARACTERS

THE STORYTELLER
THE MUSICIAN

SEDGWICK
ARCHIE WITT
CORONER
TOWN CRIER
VOICE
WOODHOUSE
WINTER
AKERMAN
MRS RIGG
BERTIE

PROLOGUE

Set: A single, old, wooden chair. A packaging crate, upended to serve as a side table. On top of the crate, three lit candles and a whisky flask.

The Musician enters.

THE BOOK OF DARKNESS & LIGHT theme

The Storyteller enters through the audience. He glares at them, occasionally pausing as if recognising faces.

As he nears the stage, he stops in front of one member of the audience and stares at them.

STORYTELLER: You look a little tense. I'm not making you nervous, am I?

There's no need to be nervous. I don't bite.

The Storyteller points at The Musician.

He bites.

The Storyteller smiles wickedly at the audience member.

You're most welcome. You're all welcome. And I expect I can guess why you're here.

You're here because you've heard tell of the book. You've come to listen to the stories. Share in the myth.

Very well.

THE BOOK *music*

According to legend there was once a book.

A cursed book whose pages were filled with wicked tales collected from all across the land, from all eras of time.

A book of stories so strange and horrifying that it had to be buried. Hidden. Laid to rest where nobody could ever find it again.

That book.

Produces the book from his coat

This book.

How it came to be in our possession… is a tale for another night.

But the legend goes that whoever possesses this book of darkness and light shall be bound to it. And sentenced to walking the land, sharing from its pages, lest the horrors within be unleashed upon him.

The legend also says that those who hear the tales shall be believers.

Or believers be made.

The Storyteller stares at a member of the audience

There's no need to look quite so worried, sir/madam. Not yet, anyway.

I'm sure we'll be alright if we stick together.

High, sustained note

But if you do feel a prickle on your neck or the leaden touch of a hand upon your shoulder... it's probably just the person behind you. Forgetting their manners.

Opens book

Let's see what the book has for us this evening...

Flicks through a few pages

Ah, [town/city]! Truly a place of troubled souls! Indeed we only need look at the people here assembled to believe it.

The Storyteller reads three short local tales or legends.

Afterwards, he slams the book closed.

The point is, the tales are everywhere. And the book has absorbed hundreds over the years.

Tonight you will hear three stories. Tales of creeping spectres. Of gruesome horrors. And of monstrous ghouls.

Perfect for the people of [town/city].

Just before we begin I feel it is my responsibility to tell you that when these stories are shared... strange and

17

unexplainable things have been known to happen.

This is your last chance to leave.

Pause

Well. If we are sitting comfortably.

Opens book – finds story, seemingly at random.

Our first tale appears to be taken from a series of legal documents and court statements. It is headed with the company details of Barchester, Magnus & Alberic, a firm of local solicitors of which you may well be aware. How this story came to be in the book will, I think, become abundantly clear.

PLAGUED

PLAGUED theme

STORYTELLER: As Secretary of State for Work and Pensions, the current spate of cuts and economic butchery have put the Right Honourable Maximilian Sedgwick MP very much in the firing line. Some of the more base and – shall we say – antagonistic tabloids have even given the effects of his recent legislation a sickly moniker: 'the Pensioner Plagues'.

Although Sedgwick's politics lean to the right, I have always found him to be a sober and more or less agreeable fellow whenever we have engaged in conversation.

The MP has been my neighbour for three years now - this property being his home away from home, of course. Yet, we have only stopped to chew the fat once or twice in that entire period. More often than not, one of us has been in a tremendous hurry to get somewhere. So, conversation has always been brief, cheerful but, it has to be said, rather insipid.

However, on the night in question at approximately twenty-past eleven, there came a violent knocking at my door. I answered it to find Sedgwick standing in a state of great distress. His skin was a sickening, greenish colour and his pupils were so dilated that I thought him certainly under the influence of some narcotic or other.

His suit was ruffled and the cuffs were damp with what I took to be rain water (for it had just started to pour down outside). But from the *smell* of the man, I realised soon enough that it was something altogether more disagreeable. There was an odd, oily sheen to the liquid and I could not place it, nor the spoiled odour it gave off.

Added to this: the man was trembling, all the while casting pitiful looks at me. As if silently appealing for help. Or mercy.

I ushered Sedgwick into my study and poured a brandy or two down him. When he had settled a little and his shivering had abated, he began to speak.

His usual, mannered rhetoric (a habit he'd picked up in parliament) was gone. His voice wavered and broke and was imbued with a wretched intensity.

SEDGWICK: It's still in there. In my house. My own house. It's still in there.

STORYTELLER: The MP went on in this way at length, with nothing of sense coming forth. I encouraged him to take a deep breath and begin again.

20

Perhaps from the point at which he had entered his house that same evening. Which, after another brandy and several stammering false starts, he did.

PLAGUED *theme extract*

According to Sedgwick, he had returned home at approximately 10.15pm, after an emergency news conference which had been held at the town hall.

Local MPs and councillors had been summoned to discuss the recent and disquieting spike in deaths of members of the older demographic in the region.

Sedgwick's opponents maintained that this distressing increase was due entirely to the conditions in which many people were latterly being forced to live. Hypothermia, influenza and malnutrition were amongst the chief assailants.

The troubling trend had been compounded by a much-publicised suicide: a ghastly incident in which a retired (and now impoverished) civil servant had apparently drowned himself in his own bathtub.

It was some two weeks before disturbed neighbours had made the putrid discovery.

Needless to say, the newspapers were at once apoplectic and giddy at the macabre

21

sensation of it all, with Sedgwick at the centre; the villain of the piece. Indeed, it would later be reported that at that same news conference, during a particularly gruesome recounting of these tragic circumstances, an evidently uninterested Sedgwick had thrown back his head and yawned rather dramatically.

Much to his colleagues' discontent, Sedgwick had managed to steal off immediately after the conference. He returned home to 'wind down' and 'get some sleep' ahead of an early start the next morning when he was due at a House debate on salaries for members of parliament.

THE HOUSE *theme*

On entering his home – so the now-broken man recounted to me as he finished his fifth brandy – Sedgwick had noticed an unusual and discernible change in the air. A dampness. A chilly, withering sensation.

He assumed the onset of a cold or fever. So, after fixing himself a hot linctus spiked with scotch, he retired immediately to bed.

However, even as he ascended the staircase to his upper floors, a queer feeling began to crowd him.

He felt almost as though he wasn't alone; as if there were a presence following him, always one step below.

Of course, he checked behind him a number of times and saw nothing at all. Perhaps he was more ill than he had first assumed.

For the briefest of moments, then, a monstrous image flooded Sedgwick's brain, bringing with it an intense feeling of nausea...

But the vile vision vanished just as soon as it had arrived, leaving the weary man with a renewed determination to be tucked up in his warm bed.

The nagging sensation of being observed was one he could not quite shake, even when he had reached the top landing.

Then, from nowhere at all, came a desperate, terrible fear of entering his own bedroom. He tried fervently to reject the silly emotion and, on reaching his door, told himself aloud *not to be a fool.*

Though a disturbing tenseness lingered, Sedgwick was a man of cold reason and he did his best to suppress the mounting panic. He edged his way, tentatively, into his room.

MOONLIGHT theme

The moonlight, breaking through the branches of the old oak tree outside Sedgwick's house, lit the room dimly. He felt for the light switch, flicked it... but found it to be of no use. A dead bulb, he told himself (and who wouldn't?). He stopped for a moment, leaning against the now-closed door, and peered into the darkness.

There was a heavy, musty smell which got on the man's chest and seemed to creep about his airways. Another symptom of his new fever, he surmised.

He took a step into the room and allowed his pupils to soak up the darkness, letting them swell and adjust to the dull light. And then he stopped dead in his tracks.

Directly ahead of Sedgwick was a large, ebony-framed mirror. What he saw reflected there made his flesh tighten and his blood sting in his veins. Over his shoulder, as he could just about make out, stood a tall and stout figure. Clad entirely in black, it appeared to be looming over him.

In horror, Sedgwick spun around, his arms flailing, his hysterical cries booming through the room; kicking and striking and screaming and struggling and... and then Sedgwick stopped.

And he laughed.

For he realised, with a significant pang of embarrassment, that he had in fact been doing battle with his best dinner jacket. He'd hung the damned thing on the back of his door in preparation for a function later in the week and had simply forgotten about it.

He chuckled to himself, entirely amused by his stupid fancy, and sat down on edge of his bed.

But in doing so, something odd made him pause.

Sedgwick lifted his right hand. He rubbed his thumb and forefinger together and noted that they were clammy. His eiderdown appeared to be wet with something dark and rather slimy. A leak? Some spillage made by his damned clumsy housekeeper?

At that very instant, Sedgwick spotted something in the tail of his eye. The moonlight was illuminating what appeared to be a trail of liquid leading from his bedroom door. It was almost as though something heavy and sodden had been dragged to his bed.

This was all becoming rather bothersome to Sedgwick. He turned to see if the dampness was isolated to the patch where he was currently sitting.

And then Sedgwick saw what he had dreaded he might, but hoped to God he would not, even as he ascended the staircase moments before. The foul image that had rushed his brain was now manifest in his bedroom.

There, in the centre of his bed, sat a man.

An old man. A wizened and gnarled figure who was slumped, strangely, forwards. He wore the remains of a tattered, cheap suit which Sedgwick could see was soaked through.

The old man stared, accusingly, from under his ancient brow.

Sedgwick had not the least idea who the man was. He was about to ask that very question when, from the back of the old man's throat, came a gurgled groan. This transformed into a deep, fearful rattle.

The politician leapt up from his usurped bed and watched in acute horror as the old man's jaw loosened and dropped to his chest with a nauseating, gristly crack.

The spectre's flesh began to flex and contract. A dark water came to the surface of its taut skin and dripped from its pores.

Sedgwick edged backwards, only as quickly as he dared; as if careful movements might pacify the monstrous thing.

His hopes were in vain. The figure on the bed began to crawl, slowly towards Sedgwick; its joints popping and creaking as it moved ever nearer.

Then, with alarming speed, the old man dashed out an arm and took hold of Sedgwick's wrist.

Its grip was bony and unrelenting and deathly cold. Sedgwick tried to shake loose of its grasp. Shaking and shaking; the sound of fragile bones creaking and crunching as he persevered. All the while, the old man on the bed was screaming and hissing vile words at the politician and just as Sedgwick thought he'd never escape the abhorrent thing's clutches... it let go.

And Sedgwick sped out of the room, down his staircase, out of his front door and over the hedge to my house, where he began his frenzied knocking.

PLAGUED theme reprise

Sedgwick yelped and twitched at the memory as he spoke. I did my best to soothe his distemper.

SEDGWICK: My name!

STORYTELLER: Sedgwick said, his speech now stilted and punctuated by the chattering of his teeth.

SEDGWICK: It was saying my name. 'SEDGWICK! SEDGWICK! YOU! YOU DID THIS!' It's still there! In my home!

STORYTELLER: At this, the politician clutched his hand to his chest and fell from his seat. The brandy glass shattered under him. I rushed over to assist the poor, frightened man.

I found him to be entirely still. When I checked for a pulse, I detected none.

And that, I swear to each of you, before almighty God himself, is how Maximilian Sedgwick's corpse came to be on my study floor.

PLAGUED theme

A lesson, perhaps, in compassion for our fellow men. Or, a fictitious cover story for a vengeful murder. You must make of the stories what you will.

GIRL, DANCING

The Storyteller flicks to another page of the book. A look of alarm and distress crosses his face.

STORYTELLER: Our next tale is taken from the abandoned journal of a noted photographer.

He and his assistant were taken to breaking into derelict buildings to capture photographs of the decaying architecture. You may well have seen some of his work. But, for the sake of his reputation, I will not reveal his identity.

This is one of the shortest and perhaps the saddest story that the book holds.

The journal entry is headed, simply: Girl, dancing.

GIRL DANCING theme

STORYTELLER: Bethany re-enters the auditorium. The camera in her hand shakes gently.

'There is a little girl dancing on the stairs,' Bethany says. Something is hiding in her voice. Something undulates behind the words.

We are photographers of the derelict; our work takes us to the underbelly of this city.

Trapped under decades of dust and fallen columns and cracked floors and broken ceilings awaits a crumbled, aching history.

Like beacons, the stories of these forgotten places call out to us. And we come.

THEATRE *theme*

A tale drew us here. To this theatre. A tale of a young girl and her step-mother who danced together on the stage.

The woman, a sensation from childhood. The girl, reared in a world where each other stage star orbited her step-mother.

And they were both blazing suns of their day.

No sooner could the child walk, she was taught to dance. Before her first words were sculpted, she had mastered ten melodies.

She became a sensation, just like her dear step-mother. All glitz and celluloid-grace.

The young girl's light grew and her energy sizzled and fizzed and her step-mother watched on and danced on and aged on.

Until, soon enough, the woman's own light faded. She became yet another peripheral star, orbiting the child.

Pride gave way to disdain and love parted for envy. And how that woman wept. And

cursed in secret as her step-daughter's
stardom began to eclipse her own.

MOURNING theme

And there was a great fire.

The crate glows orange as if ablaze.

A great fire in the great theatre.

The girl, sent to the stairwell to rehearse her
art between the acts, was trapped between
two locked doors.

Two doors that were never locked.

Smoke began to fill the space. It crept
through the cracks and gaps in the door
frames. Yet, the child did not stop her
practice.

Even when the thick smog began to pour into
her little lungs, she persevered. Coughing but
not faltering; a beautiful, deathly spectacle.

The little girl, dancing, ignorant of the
desperate evacuation taking place on the
other side of those doors.

Only, minutes later, she could dance no more.
Nor move. Nor breathe. Nor live.

INFERNO music

Out on the street stood the company and the
audience. Safe and startled.

31

The step-mother, her cheeks streaked with strange tears, asking each person: 'Have you seen her? Have you seen her?'

Deep inside her heart: a dark and terrible secret.

Deep inside her pocket: a key, a book of matches.

And the flames and the heat and the smoke swelled on.

The crate light fades

That story drew us here, to this theatre. And here we stand, my partner and I, ready to begin work. Lenses cleaned and cameras poised.

Bethany re-enters the charred auditorium. The camera in her hand shakes gently. There's something hiding in her voice. Something undulates behind the words.

'There is a little girl dancing on the stairs. She says she died here.'

GIRL DANCING *theme reprise*

Blackout

THE BONEHOUSE

STORYTELLER: We come now to our final and perhaps most peculiar tale. And it comes with a warning from me. If, at any point during this story, you feel something take hold of your hand... do not look at it.

The Storyteller goes to speak again but stops

When the book came into our possession, I found, tucked into its pages, dozens of strange fragments. But, until very recently, I thought these documents to be meaningless. A slew of gruesome, unintelligible outpourings. And so they have never been shared with the world. Until now.

I had to go to great pains to reassemble them into a coherent account.

BONE music

I felt much like an archaeologist must when discovering the remains of some long-dead beast. Initially, a bone here, a tooth there. But, with the application of much patience, a skeleton begins to emerge. I shall have to rely on you all to lay on the flesh.

This is a story made up of those fragments. And the first I wish to share with you comes from a manuscript of a book which, according to my own research, has never been published. It was written by a historian by the name of J. Archibald Witt and it refers to this.

The Storyteller takes out a hand-drawn image of a roundhouse lock-up; passes it around the audience.

This is a roundhouse lock-up.

Many of these structures are still in existence, though not used for their original purposes. This first extract goes into some detail about the uses of these so-called roundhouses.

Produces a fragment of paper

ROUNDHOUSE *theme*

(*Reads*) Perhaps the most interesting method of incarceration of this period was the Roundhouse. The structures were often, as the name suggests, round in design and typically not greater than ten feet in diameter nor height. The inside was most often without light at all. This gave rise to the nickname 'blindhouse' which, along with 'watch-house', 'guardhouse' and this writer's favourite 'bonehouse', fell quickly into popular use. Any lawbreakers caught in the villages and towns where such a lock-up was situated would be remanded inside until at least the following morning when a magistrate would deal with them. They were unsanitary places, even beyond barnyard standards; often riddled with the stench of human effluence. Lord preserve any poor soul who was locked inside one of the infernal places and forgotten about for any significant length of time.

A fragment from 'Punishment and Repentance: A Study of Prisons, Jails and Lock-Ups 1500 - 1950' by J. Archibald Witt.

Now follows a series of letters written by Archibald Witt to his former teacher, who he refers to as 'Bertie' throughout.

THE BONEHOUSE *motif*

ARCHIE WITT: 3rd February 1953

Dearest Bertie,

You will remember that I delivered my lecture on the 'Roundhouses of the British Isles' last Michaelmas eve. Well, a good deal has passed off in the meantime regarding my research and something of a breakthrough is on the horizon. Indeed, I have taken steps to go to the very root of the tree. You would be proud of me, old friend!

ABBOT'S KNOCK *texture*

You may recall that I fleetingly referred to the roundhouse in the small village of Abbot's Knock in the lecture, of which very little is currently known.

35

The village is set in a crevice of the landscape in central Swithinshire. Quite a picturesque town, in actual fact, with the most beautiful, savage country surrounding it. I shall be taking myself out for many a ramble during my stay.

That is to say that I will be going to Abbot's Knock this weekend and staying for as long as is necessary to build up an accurate understanding of certain documents which have come into my possession in recent weeks.

Old Daniel Burnage at the central library happened upon several curious, waxed-sealed boxes when clearing out his archives. Blow me, Bertie, if several of them weren't full of odds and sods pertaining to Swithinshire and, in particular, to Abbot's Knock! Old Burnage claims he has no idea how they got there. The curious grin of fortune!

Much of the content of the boxes is dreary and useless: endless minuted town meetings and dull-as-ditchwater financial audits. But in and amongst the tedium are a number of fascinating and, in some cases, chilling accounts of judicial process in the village.

In particular, there are many dozens of documents relating to the very bonehouse whose history has eluded me for so long. I am, you might imagine, delighted with the find.

PACKING music

> I have just noticed the time; I must make haste now to prepare for my trip. I will write more from the train — there are four connections on my journey south, if you can credit that. I have all of the documents packed up to bring along. Nothing quite like primary research, would you not agree, old teacher?
>
> Yours always,
>
> Archie

The sound of a train's whistle in the distance; the train comes thundering past.

Carriage noise continues

ARCHIE WITT: 5th February 1953

> Dearest Bertie,
>
> I must say, the journey into Swithinshire has been a pretty one. God's paintbrush has been overworked on these landscapes! The lushness of home is not quite as evident here, but the muted greens and browns certainly carve an impression. A lot of mills on this route, too.
>
> I'm presently on the second leg of the journey — the longest — and have opened my travel bureau to write to you. I am brimming with excitement to see the roundhouse at Abbot's Knock in just a few hours.

I mean to check into my rooms as soon as I arrive (which I am excited to report look directly onto the market square and, therefore, the roundhouse) and then go immediately to see the building. I wish to inspect the site on which it is built as closely as is possible. You see, I've discovered something rather intriguing, old friend, and it is this:

According to one of the documents in Old Burnage's boxes – a journal of sorts – the roundhouse was built where a great tree once stood. I suspect you can guess the rest but, in case you can't: the tree was also the site of the wrath of justice. It was a hanging tree, Bertie!

REV. HOLBEIN'S *theme*

The town magistrate (from 1695 to 1717) was one Rev. Patrick Holbein. He was the self-designated hangman. The same journal hints at the idea that the fiend rather enjoyed his work, too. A macabre detail, here recorded, is that Holbein was said to cut off and keep a lock of the hair of every person he put to death. I wonder where the awful collection is now. I will, of course, ask at the village museum. A mention of publication in a book often opens doors and loosens tongues, as well you know.

One thing is for certain, this Holbein fellow was a most foul individual. His death toll on the charge of witchcraft alone approaches two-hundred and eighty – which, I think, brings him close to Matthew Hopkins' total, does it not? Seems Holbein travelled up and down the land hunting out witches and warlocks, carting them back to Abbot's Knock for trial and execution.

I have a copy of the Reverend's death certificate here. It seems Holbein met a rather grisly end himself. He was found in his rooms by the village Beadle after failing to attend a case hearing.

CORONER: At a quarter to three in the afternoon, Beadle Coupe did enter the rooms of Reverend Patrick Holbein. The Beadle did find Rev. Holbein, face-down on the floor, lifeless and still. The Beadle did send for Dr. John Sheerman, the surgeon, who pronounced Holbein dead at the scene.

His body was discovered to be exsanguinated where it lay, though no puncture mark was found on the flesh. Neither was there a drop of blood about the body nor in the building nor the outside yard.

The physician did also note that Holbein's face was wrenched and contorted, suggesting that he did die in acute agony, though no cogent physical evidence of such an end was in presentation.

ARCHIE WITT: Very curious, no?

The hanging tree was uprooted soon after Holbein's death and the roundhouse built in its place. Quite the discovery, you must admit, Bertie! How silly and superstitious were the people of that era.

There are reams and reams of paper left to sift through. I'm in heaven.

BLACK CLOUD *music*

It seems the Lord has pulled across the curtains here in Swithinshire. The clouds are looking very angry indeed. Let's hope this is not an omen of any kind.

Yours always,

Archie.

STORYTELLER: Incidentally, I'm sure you are aware, but in the spirit of removing any doubt, the term *exsanguinated* – the state in which Rev. Holbein's body was found – means drained of blood.

REV. HOLBEIN'S *theme reprise*

ARCHIE WITT: 7th February 1953

Dearest Bertie,

I've had quite the few days, I can tell you! I'm established at a rather fancy antique writing desk (which my hosts, Mr and Mrs Rigg, have set up especially for me). They claim, if you can believe it, that the desk is made from timber salvaged from the same hanging tree I mentioned in my last letter!

THE DESK *texture*

It's been in their family for donkey's years, apparently. What an apt and grisly thing! Every now and then a faint waft of something malodorous drifts up from it. Apart from this, it's quite a delight.

The lodgings are very much to my satisfaction, with my only gripe being that the bathroom is a shared one. Still, I seem to be the only guest in residence at the present moment and it is only a short walk along the landing.

My hosts are rather pleasant, if a little taciturn. (I think there may have been some crossed wires about my profession. Mrs Rigg seemed to be entirely convinced that I was a cartographer. When I told her that I was nothing of the kind, but a *historian*, she became somewhat uninterested).

My rooms are above a bakery, run by the Riggs, and so the smells of baking dough are ever-present. It makes one's stomach growl almost perpetually. I also have the most wonderful fireplace, which I will be making use of as the nights continue to draw colder.

Archie moves to the window, gazes out of it.

I'm looking, now, out of my window and I can see the object of my academic affections, as it were. The roundhouse is but a stone's throw away. It's really rather pleasing. At night, two street lamps illuminate the structure magnificently.

I have not yet managed to make a full investigation of the lock-up since from the moment I stepped off the train in Abbot's Knock to the present it has been pouring with rain. I wish to see the thing's beautiful details in good light (and, preferably, with dry feet).

No matter, my own enforced lock-in has obliged me to make the most of the materials I found in Old Burnage's boxes.

It seems, Bertie, that the Abbot's Knock of old was a rather cruel township. There are over a dozen examples of prisoners being left in the roundhouse far, far longer than ever ought to have been necessary. And for the silliest of crimes! One fellow was reportedly incarcerated for 'demonstrable laziness'. I'll continue to report what I discover.

Tomorrow a meeting has been arranged for me with the village's lay-historian, a chap by the name of Akerman. We're going to 'share notes', as it were.

Yours always,

Archie

THE CHILD theme

> PS: I do not think much of attitudes towards parenting here in this village! Very late indeed, during both of the nights of my stay, as I have gazed out onto the roundhouse from my room, I have seen the same child. A small boy. Standing in front of the bonehouse. He was staring at the door.

> I mentioned the child to Mrs Rigg this morning over breakfast, but as the poor thing was facing away from me on both occasions, I had very few details to offer. At any rate, Mrs Rigg, rather curtly, said that she didn't know *which little boy* I was talking about and then she hurried away to add another batch of dough to the oven.

> It's rather strange, Bertie: I do not remember telling Mrs Rigg it was a little boy.

THE BONEHOUSE theme

ARCHIE WITT: 9th February 1953

SUN ON THE MARKET SQUARE music

> My dear Bertie,

> I've finally conducted my first set of observations of the lock-up. What a

beautiful, terrible thing it is. The sun shone on me all morning. The brickwork is rather stunning in such light. The pointing looks as though it may have been completed yesterday. Even the roof is in a marvellous condition.

The Abbot's Knock bonehouse is one of those without a window – which, as we've always agreed, would have made being contained in it almost unbearable.

There are four stone steps leading up to the entrance. The door itself, Mrs Rigg has told me, is original. It, too, is made of wood taken from the hanging tree, just like my writing desk.

I have not, as yet, been able to get a straight answer about gaining access to the interior. Mr Rigg has told me that he doesn't know who, if anyone, might have a key. Which seems absurd to me. But, I shan't give up, Bertie! We'll get in there, yet. Whether by key or by devilry or by axe!

Music stops

The closest I have come to getting inside the damned thing was a sneaky glimpse through the key hole. I paced up to the frightful door when nobody was about and had a long peer inside.

ARCHIE looks inside the bonehouse. What he sees chills him to the bone. He takes a moment or two to get his breath back.

> And here is the damnedest thing, old friend: there was something in there.

Short, sharp trill

> Something, I'd be prepared to swear, *moved* from one side to the other. A shadow. A bird, perhaps.

> Although it did proceed rather slowly and oddly for a bird.

> There must be a break in the walls. The poor thing must have pushed its way inside. And is now unable to get out again.

> I fear that if I do not get hold of that elusive key, the little beast will die.

> Makes one wonder how many other souls have perished in there.

> Well. I shall have to bring a hanky to cover my mouth and nose when we finally get the door open.

SUN ON THE MARKET SQUARE music

> Incidentally, Mr Akerman at the museum is a splendid fellow. He shares our enthusiasm for historical tittle-tattle and agrees that it's in the ephemera where the real meat is to be found.

45

He's not from Abbot's Knock originally but settled here twenty or so years ago. He seems to have what I can only describe as a bitter affection for the locals!

Like a true gentleman, he had taken the time to dig out a few intriguing papers and artefacts for me to get my teeth into, which I'll share in due course.

For now, I enclose a most curious facsimile. You remember the old fiend Rev. Holbein? Well, this village notice pertains to the final execution he performed. The last hanging before the roundhouse was erected.

Take a look at the woman in question's name: Nan Malvat.

Of what extraction might that name be, old friend? I wonder if you can shed any light on her country of origin? It would be tremendously helpful for my research.

I'll leave you to puzzle.

Yours always,

Archie

PS: That child was outside again last night, staring at the roundhouse door. This time, a little further away from it. That is to say, a little closer to my lodgings.

MALVAT'S theme

TOWN CRIER: ABBOT'S KNOCK. TOWN NOTICES. FEBRUARY 14th 1717:

Tuesday last, in the morning, a nuisance vagrant who identified herself as Nan Malvat was hanged until dead in the village square.

Accused of witchcraft, the woman was offered several opportunities to confess her crimes by prosecutor Rev. Patrick Holbein.

However, the woman simply repeated her own name over and over, in an animated and ghastly fashion, pointing manically into thin air.

As per his custom, Rev. Holbein took a lock of Malvat's hair prior to her execution, holding it up for the village onlookers to see. The witch's body was burned thereafter.

Malvat failed the test by pricking and several witch marks were found about her body when stripped. Since Malvat's arrival in Abbot's Knock, the deaths of four men, two women, one child and nine cattle have plagued the village. Each victim, man and beast, was found drained of blood.

Malvat had been spotted in the village on several occasions before her apprehension, along with her child whose whereabouts cannot now be verified.

THE DREAM music

Archie appears to be exhausted and traumatised.

ARCHIE WITT: 12th February 1953

My dear friend Bertie,

A brief missive today, I'm afraid. I have not passed a good night since Monday (today being Thursday). I have rather fallen into a ghastly habit of waking at the same time each morning: just after 3am. Always with a terrible thirst.

Two nights ago, I had a most hideous dream. I woke – or, I fancied that I did – in utter darkness. Freezing and with a stench surrounding me the like of which I cannot even begin to describe.

I lay on my back in a fearful fever. Staring upwards. As my eyes began to adjust to the darkness, I saw – and I know just how preposterous it sounds – I saw the form of a person hovering above me.

Although the face was obscured I could tell from its long, dark hair that it was a woman. And I knew from the pallor of her flesh that she was dead.

THE BODY DESCENDS music

She began to descend. Lower and lower she came. I found myself quite unable to move and barely able to breathe. She was getting closer and closer and closer and closer.

And then she was *on* me. This dead, rotting body lying atop my own, smothering me. I took in a deep breath, whereupon I felt that my mouth was suddenly full of thick, coarse hair.

Archie begins to choke. He stands up. After a moment, he produces from his throat a long, dreadful rope of black and matted hair.

He screams and flings it away.

There's a long pause. We glimpse The Storyteller beneath his performance of Archie Witt. He composes himself.

ARCHIE WITT: This time I was certainly awake.

VOICE: (*Whispered*) Nan Malvat…

ARCHIE WITT: But then, from the darkness of my room, the sound of a whisper drifted to my ears; the echo of the dream, perhaps, but I'd wager my very soul that the words were discernible and that they were: Nan Malvat.

The name of that poor wretch from the newspaper clipping.

It seemed to be coming from the writing desk, Bertie.

When, after a short while, I had returned to my senses, I went to collect some water as my jug was empty.

On returning to my room, I felt somehow drawn to the window. There again, outside, was the child. Again facing away. Again a little closer to the bakery. Almost directly in front of it, in fact. I rapped on the window to get his attention and shoo him away. He did not turn around.

But, he did hear me, Bertie. I know this because he raised his little hand and gave a sort of backwards wave to me. The sight of the poor thing makes me feel ill at ease. Sickened, somehow.

Perhaps it was the hour and the light.

He ought to be indoors!

I really must go and rest now, old friend. I'm more than slightly pathetic when deprived of sleep.

Yours,

Archie

MANY HAPPY RETURNS theme

Archie seems dazed but attempting normality.

ARCHIE WITT: 14th February 1953

My dear Bertie,

Happy Birthday, you old devil! Many happy returns and I'm sorry that I can't be with you to celebrate today. If you'll have me, I'll pass through on my way back up north and I can make merry with you and Alice then. It will be splendid to see you both.

Remarkable, isn't it, how much good a full night's sleep can do? Aside from my 3am awakenings – which I've simply accepted as a part of my Abbot's Knock routine – I slept rather well for two nights running.

Another spot of good news, however, incidental, is that the child was not out in the market square at all last night nor the night before. Not that I saw, at any rate.

I've been able to put pen to paper on a chapter draft today, which is most encouraging. And I put in another visit with Mr Akerman at the museum. He is taking a trip in the next week and has kindly left me with enough resources to keep me busy. He's left me his forwarding address for his residence in Scotland, should I have any pressing questions.

Mr Akerman has uncovered some rather fascinating instances of criminals who were imprisoned in the bonehouse. It seems that, in several cases, people emerged from the lock-up rather psychologically disturbed. Allow me to give you some examples.

One man, a Melvyn Woodhouse, who was locked up for scrumping apples in 1730, gave the following testimony:

WOODHOUSE: The moment I stepped in it, I knew something was up. I couldn't get no rest at all, sir, and it weren't the smell or the muck. After a bit, me legs started to buckle, sir, I was forced to sit down. I felt it soon as I put my hand down to sit. It was all over the floor! I knew what it was at once, sir. The floor was covered with hair! Human hair! It was all over the floor! Please don't send me back in it, sir, I'll be good now! I promise I will!

ARCHIE WITT: The lad's testimony put me in mind of my own horrific dream. A chilling coincidence.

Another testimony tells of a young woman, one Jennifer Winter, accused of pilfering from her employer. She had been locked up on a Thursday eve and forgotten about until Monday morning.

When the door was finally opened, the woman was discovered wedged down in the drain of the bonehouse. Barely alive.

Again, a fragment from her testimony below:

WINTER: There was something else in there with me. I swear on this Bible here. It would not leave me be. Not for a minute. Kept trying to take a hold of my hand. I paced around inside for as long as I could, trying to escape its grasp. But every time I stopped moving, it grabbed at me again. It was driving me to despair. I had to get out. And the drain was the only way I could think of doing it.

ARCHIE WITT: Plenty more to go over, old friend. Back to it for me. Once again, many happy returns.

Yours always,

Archie

STORYTELLER: Here, there's rather a jump in time. And no letters were exchanged for quite a number of days. We return to find Archibald Witt a rather transformed character.

ARCHIE TRANSFORMED music

Archie is a different man. Dishevelled and frightened, almost child-like.

ARCHIE WITT: 1st March 1953

Bertie,

Something most unsettling is happening here. I am continuing my research but I feel that I am being plagued. It's the child, Bertie! Don't think me mad. I had supposed that of myself already and surely, in doing so, have vindicated myself as sane.

Mischief. Mischief!

Last night I woke at three as usual and went to collect water. On my route back, I happened to look upon the staircase that leads down into the bakery.

He was standing there, Bertie. Facing away from me.

I studied him. His flesh is pallid, almost translucent. His hair is greasy and brittle-looking. And his clothes are not of today, Bertie.

He reached his hand backwards and held it there. As if he wanted me to take it. As if he to lead me somewhere!

It put the very fear of God into me and I ran back to my room, locking the door behind me.

Archie cowers.

A monstrous thought has occurred to me. Those nights when the child was not outside, on the market square. Was it because he was already in the house?

I fear, old friend, that he is... oh, I cannot even say the word.

Restless. Wandering.

Perhaps he is some orphaned child. Perhaps his mother or father died in that lock-up. If I could only open that door...

Something occurs to Archie and, for a moment, he is back to his old, rational self.

I will write to Mr Akerman and find out, if I can, who he is. Which poor soul he may belong to.

Perhaps that will give me peace. Perhaps it will give us both peace.

Yours, Archie.

AKERMAN: 7th March 1953

Dear Mr Witt,

Thank you for your letter. I am due at my aunt's house in a short while and shall keep my response to you brief.

To my knowledge, and as far as my research has stretched, nobody has died in the roundhouse at Abbot's Knock. Are you quite sure that this child is not a relative of the Riggs?

I must say, your letter had me quite worried about you.

I suggest a good tonic, plenty of sleep and perhaps you ought now to return home? The Swithinshire air plainly does not agree with you.

Sincerely and with concern,

Gerald Akerman

STORYTELLER: The date here is assumed to be 13th March 1953.

The scene is entirely black except for a candle that Archie holds tightly.

ARCHIE WITT: Bertie,

Help me!

Low, rumbling tone.

A horror of horrors is unfurling before me. I am now on my tenth night without anything resembling sleep. In my waking hours, I can barely move from my bed. I am beset by a terrible weakness.

I am not sure which things are real and which are figments of my imagination.

I keep returning to the account of Nan Malvat. Those lines, Bertie. (*whispered*) About the child:

TOWN CRIER: ...Malvat had been spotted in the village on several occasions, along with her child whose whereabouts cannot now be verified...

ARCHIE WITT: I have had to tear that desk apart, Bertie. The stench coming from it! Death. Death! And the voices. The whispering. *I could not bear it!*

I have burned all of those wretched documents. That wretched book.

Music swells

> Thank God that the door is locked! Last night there was a sound coming from it. A scratching sound.

A most terrible scratching sound.

> Then, knocking. Dreadful, endless knocking.

The sound of violent, urgent knocking on the door.

STORYTELLER: A huge swathe of text is indecipherable here. It is struck out with black ink. The letter picks up, apparently on the next day.

ARCHIE WITT: Jesus, God, Bertie. They've taken my key away. I am left defenceless!

> In the dead of night, I awoke to find *him* standing at the foot of my bed. Again facing away. He reached out to me.

> And then he turned around.

> His *face*, Bertie!

> Something is terribly wrong with his face!

> I know tonight will be the end of it.

Music ends

STORYTELLER: Here, Mr Witt appears to have written NAN MALVAT over and over again on the page. And then, finally, two sentences scribbled in an almost unrecognisable hand.

> It is 3am. He is here.

THE CHILD *theme*

MRS RIGG *music*

MRS RIGG: 15th March 1953

Dear Sir,

My name is Emily Rigg and I am writing to you for your assistance with your friend, Mr Archibald Witt. You may be aware that he has been lodging in our rooms for a number of weeks. He has become, I'm afraid to say, quite ill indeed. Most alarmingly so, in fact. Raving during the day and roaming the halls at night.

Two days ago, for his own safety, we took away the key to his bedroom. However, this only served to whip Mr Witt into a rage. He began shouting obscenities, insisting that my husband and I had, to quote Mr Witt directly, *murdered him.*

Yesterday morning, we sent for the doctor, having heard much screaming and commotion from Mr Witt's room during the night. When the doctor arrived, however, we found the room to be empty. Mr Witt could not be found anywhere.

The room was left in a terrible state. The bed was covered in a mass of thick, black hair. We've not the least idea from where he might have procured such a horrid mess.

Despite our own setbacks and upset, we are, understandably, frightfully worried for Mr Witt. If you can offer any assistance or insight, I should be greatly appreciative.

Yours faithfully,

Mrs Emily Rigg

PS: I have enclosed some pieces of note paper in this envelope which appear to be addressed to you, although the format and content is most queer.

STORYTELLER: *(Produces a newspaper clipping)* The penultimate fragment of this story is a cutting from a newspaper, *The Swithinshire Chronicle*, dated four months after the disappearance of Archibald Witt.

(*Reads*) Swithinshire Chronicle

THE DISCOVERY theme

Police officers are conducting an investigation after human remains were discovered in the Roundhouse lock-up in the village of Abbot's Knock.

The remains are understood to be the body of historian J. Archibald Witt who visited the village four months previously. Both members of the local police and villagers are baffled by the devastating discovery, since the lock-up has been sealed off since 1875.

The door had to be torn off the structure to gain access. Mr Witt's body was said to have been in a remarkable state of preservation on account of it having been, inexplicably, drained of blood.

Along with the remains, a number of papers and documents were discovered in the lock-up, including a peculiar book. The investigation is ongoing.

Single, high note

BERTIE: My dear Archie,

Thank you for the birthday wishes, dear boy. You are most kind indeed.

And, yes, Alice and I would be thrilled to have you come visiting on your route home.

Now, to the business of this poor woman. What a shameful era in our country's history.

These words: Nan Malvat. On closer inspection, it appears to me that the first word, most likely, does not say *nan* but *nen*. And, if you look attentively, you'll see that the village notice's typeset is rather an odd one, perhaps leading to the confusion.

At any rate, the language is Catalan. Also, dear Archie, *nen malvat* is not a name at all.

It seems odd to me that the woman should have been screaming this at her execution. In fact, I doubt that to be the case since the direct translation of *nen malvat* is: wicked child.

Hope this is of some small help. Do take good care of yourself and I shall see you soon.

My very best,

Bertie

THE DISCOVERY *theme*

EPILOGUE

STORYTELLER: So ends the tragic tale of J. Archibald Witt. And indeed, so ends our little evening of stories.

Thank you for listening. I trust we have made believers of you?

You are now all free to leave.

We, on the other hand...

THE BOOK music reprise

According to legend there was once a book.

A cursed book whose pages were filled with wicked tales collected from all across the land, from all eras of time.

A book of stories so strange and horrifying that it had to be buried. Hidden. Laid to rest where nobody could ever find it again.

That book.

This book.

How it came to be in our possession... is a tale for another night.

The Storyteller slams the book closed.

Blackout.

END.